STAR WARS ®

A NEW HOPE

STAR WARS

A NEW HOPE

SCRIPT
BRUCE JONES

PENCILS
EDUARDO BARRETO

INKS
EDUARDO BARRETO
AL WILLIAMSON
CARLOS GARZÓN

COLORS
JAMES SINCLAIR
CARY PORTER

LETTERING
STEVE DUTRO

COVER ART
GREG & TIM HILDEBRANDT

BASED ON THE GEORGE LUCAS MOVIE, *STAR WARS*®

BOXTREE

PUBLISHER
MIKE RICHARDSON

SERIES EDITOR
BOB COOPER

SERIES ASSISTANT EDITOR
DAVID LAND

COLLECTION EDITOR
LYNN ADAIR

COLLECTION DESIGN
SCOTT TICE

COLLECTION DESIGN MANAGER
BRIAN GOGOLIN

SPECIAL THANKS TO
LUCY AUTREY WILSON AND ALLAN KAUSCH
AT LUCASFILM

Dark Horse Comics, Inc.
Neil Hankerson executive vice president • David Scroggy vice president of publishing
Lou Bank vice president of sales & marketing • Andy Karabatsos vice president of finance
Mark Anderson general counsel • Meloney C. Chadwick director of editorial adm.
Randy Stradley creative director • Cindy Marks director of production & design
Mark Cox art director • Sean Tierney computer graphics director
Michael Martens director of sales • Tod Borleske director of licensing
Mark Ellington director of operations • Dale LaFountain director of m.i.s.

This book collects issues one through four of the Dark Horse comic-book series
Star Wars®: A New Hope Special Edition.

A CIP catalogue entry for this book is available from the British Library.

First published in Great Britain by
Boxtree Limited
Broadwall House
21 Broadwall
London SE1 9PL

First edition: January 1997
ISBN: 0-7522-2343-7

10 9 8 7 6 5 4 3 2 1

Printed in Canada

The story of Dark Horse Comics' adaptation of *A New Hope* The Special Edition actually begins nearly twenty years ago . . .

In late 1977, several months after *Star Wars* had already become a bona fide theatrical hit, comic-book artist Al Williamson was contacted by Lucasfilm to do some art samples for the already-in-production *Star Wars* newspaper strip. Thrilled that George Lucas had taken an interest in his work, Williamson contacted his good friend, writer Archie Goodwin, and asked him to help put together some sample strips. It didn't take any deliberation on Lucasfilm's part before offering the two production of the daily and Sunday *Star Wars* strip.

Unfortunately, Williamson had to decline since he was under contract to King Features drawing the "Secret Agent X-9" strip and really didn't feel like quitting. He decided to stick with something familiar and enjoyable rather than taking on something that would likely turn out to be as major a commitment as *Star Wars*. So, in the late 1970s, comics fans were introduced to *Star Wars* by Roy Thomas and Howard Chaykin's best-selling comics adaptation from Marvel Comics. This was followed by a very well-received monthly comic-book series, which included artwork by Chaykin, Carmine Infantino, Walt Simonson, Herb Trimpe, Tom Palmer, Mike Vosburg, and Michael Golden. Russ Manning's elegantly drawn *Star Wars* newspaper strip made its debut shortly thereafter.

Finally, in 1980, with the release of *The Empire Strikes Back*, events transpired to allow Williamson to draw the Marvel comics adaptation based on pal Archie Goodwin's script. Shortly thereafter, due to Russ Manning's failing health, Williamson and Goodwin took over work on the daily *Star Wars* newspaper strip in 1981, producing a memorable three-and-a-half-year run. When *Return of the Jedi* was released in 1983, there really wasn't any other choice than Goodwin and Williamson to do the comics adaptation.

By 1990, Dark Horse Comics had acquired the license to produce *Star Wars* comics. One of the first projects was reprinting, in color, the early '80s Goodwin/Williamson newspaper strips. At publisher Mike Richardson's request, Williamson took a hand reformatting the strips to fit the new comic-book format, and he contributed fourteen brand-new pieces of cover art for the twenty-issue series and three-volume collected set. Shortly thereafter, Dark Horse decided to reprint the Marvel *Star Wars* comics adaptations in a deluxe format with new interior coloring, and Williamson contributed new cover art for the *Empire Strikes Back* and *Return of the Jedi* volumes.

During summer 1995, Lucasfilm announced that in 1997 — in conjunction with the twentieth anniversary of the release of the original *Star Wars* movie — it would release expanded and updated versions of the three *Star Wars* movies. Dark Horse immediately made plans for a new comics adaptation of the first movie, incorporating the footage and new characters Lucasfilm was adding to the film. As editor of Dark Horse's *Star Wars* comics, I could think of no one other than Williamson — who had always lamented the fact that he'd missed the opportunity to draw *A New Hope* — to illustrate this new adaptation.

With a fair amount of lead time, I called Williamson and began a long process of talking him into doing the project. I knew going in that his decade-long working relationship with Marvel could preclude his involvement. The decision weighed heavily on Williamson for several months. After dozens of phone calls back and forth, he finally called in early January 1996 to decline, claiming that he'd already felt the same sort of anxiety start to build up in anticipation of doing this project as it had prior to working on the two-issue *Flash Gordon* project he'd drawn for Marvel in 1995. For this reason, rather than because of time conflicts or his existing Marvel relationship, he decided to forego working on the special edition of *A New Hope*. He just didn't feel like he'd be able to do the job as well as he would like to — and as well as the job deserved to be done.

In his heart, Williamson earnestly wanted to draw *Star Wars* again, yet he knew deep down that he wouldn't be able to do it. We tossed around the names of artists who might be up to the task. "Who worked on the *Aliens/Predator: The Deadliest of the Species* series a year or so ago?" "Eduardo Barreto, " I replied. "And, yeah, I think he'd do a great job!" So I called Barreto, who said he was finishing up work for a couple of other publishers and would love nothing more than to devote *all* of his time to drawing the new adaptation of *Star Wars* — a movie he absolutely loved!

To coincide with Lucasfilm's goal of releasing *A New Hope* The Special Edition in May 1997, Dark Horse was still planning a May 1997 release for the comics series. Barreto had started work on the series and was nearly finished with his pencils for the first of four issues when Lucasfilm announced that it was moving up the film's release date to February 1997. To keep the comics on schedule, I was going to have to hire an inker to work over Barreto's pencils, allowing the creative work to progress at a pace almost twice as fast as originally planned.

Enter Al Williamson, stage right. And this time it worked. Schedules dovetailed perfectly, and Al was absolutely committed to the opportunity to contribute inks over Barreto's pencils — to finally complete his personal cycle of work on the *Star Wars* trilogy. And when Lucasfilm moved up the release date yet again, to January, it became necessary to ask Williamson's longtime friend and collaborator Carlos Garzón to help with the inking for issues #3 and 4 of the series. It was becoming more and more like old-home week, as Garzón had worked with Williamson on the Marvel adaptations of *The Empire Strikes Back* and *Return of the Jedi*.

Hopefully, the readers will be just as happy as I am with the results: the classical artistry Al Williamson brings to the project, the sterling script adaptation by Bruce Jones, the gorgeously detailed pencilling wizardry of Eduardo Barreto, Dave Dorman's amazing set of interlocking covers for the comic-book series and Tim and Greg Hildebrandt's stunning cover for this volume, lettering by Steve Dutro — who's by far the most efficient, precise, and talented letterer with whom I've ever had the pleasure of working — and of course, the rich palettes of colorists James Sinclair and Cary Porter.

Enjoy!

Bob Cooper

A long time ago in a galaxy far, far away. . . .

DURING THE BATTLE, REBEL SPIES MANAGED TO STEAL SECRET PLANS TO THE EMPIRE'S ULTIMATE WEAPON, THE **DEATH STAR**, AN ARMORED SPACE STATION WITH ENOUGH POWER TO DESTROY AN ENTIRE PLANET.

PURSUED BY THE EMPIRE'S SINISTER AGENTS, PRINCESS LEIA RACES HOME ABOARD HER STARSHIP, CUSTODIAN OF THE STOLEN PLANS THAT CAN SAVE HER PEOPLE AND RESTORE FREEDOM TO THE GALAXY...

WHAT A DESOLATE PLACE THIS IS! ARTOO, WHERE DO YOU THINK YOU'RE GOING?

BEEP! CHIRP! SKREEP!

TATOOINE, IN THE JUNDLAND REGION, WHERE THE ENDLESS DESERT MEETS THE FOREBODING DUNE SEA...

WHAT MAKES YOU THINK THERE ARE SETTLEMENTS OVER THERE?

WHAT MISSION? WHAT ARE YOU TALKING ABOUT? I'VE JUST ABOUT HAD ENOUGH OF YOU! GO THAT WAY!

CHIRP! TWEEE!

YOU'LL BE MALFUNCTIONING WITHIN A DAY, YOU NEARSIGHTED SCRAP PILE!

AND DON'T LET ME CATCH YOU FOLLOWING ME BEGGING FOR HELP...

...BECAUSE YOU WON'T GET IT!

SOME TIME LATER...

THAT MALFUNCTIONING LITTLE TWERP! THIS IS ALL HIS FAULT!

WAIT, WHAT'S THAT?

OVER HERE! HEY! HELP! PLEASE HELP!

WHILE ELSEWHERE...

CHIRP... TWEET... TWEEE...

NAGHHH!

THE JUNDLAND WASTES ARE NOT TO BE TRAVELED LIGHTLY. TELL ME, YOUNG LUKE, WHAT BRINGS YOU OUT THIS FAR?

BEN? BEN KENOBI?

OH, THIS LITTLE DROID! I THINK HE'S SEARCHING FOR HIS FORMER MASTER...CLAIMS TO BE THE PROPERTY OF AN OBI-WAN KENOBI.

IS HE A RELATIVE OF YOURS?

OBI-WAN... NOW THAT'S A NAME I'VE NOT HEARD IN A LONG TIME.

YOU KNOW HIM?

WELL, OF COURSE. HE'S ME! I HAVEN'T GONE BY THE NAME OBI-WAN SINCE, OH, BEFORE YOU WERE BORN.

THEN THE DROID DOES BELONG TO YOU.

DON'T SEEM TO REMEMBER EVER OWNING A DROID. VERY INTERESTING.

THREEPIO!

I THINK WE BETTER GET INDOORS.

WHERE AM I? I MUST'VE TAKEN A BAD STEP...

THE SAND PEOPLE WILL SOON BE BACK AND IN GREATER NUMBERS.

THE DEATH STAR CONFERENCE ROOM...

THE IMPERIAL SENATE WILL NO LONGER BE OF ANY CONCERN TO US. THE REGIONAL GOVERNORS NOW HAVE DIRECT CONTROL OVER THEIR TERRITORIES. FEAR WILL KEEP THE LOCAL SYSTEMS IN LINE. FEAR OF THIS BATTLE STATION.

GRAND MOFF TARKIN, IF THE REBELS HAVE OBTAINED A COMPLETE TECHNICAL READOUT OF THIS STATION, THEY MIGHT FIND A WEAKNESS AND--

THE PLANS, COMMANDER TAGGE, WILL SOON BE BACK IN OUR HANDS.

THIS STATION IS NOW THE ULTIMATE POWER IN THE UNIVERSE. I SUGGEST WE USE IT!

DON'T BE TOO PROUD OF THIS TECHNOLOGICAL TERROR YOU'VE CONSTRUCTED, ADMIRAL MOTTI.

THE ABILITY TO DESTROY A PLANET IS INSIGNIFICANT NEXT TO THE POWER OF THE FORCE.

DON'T TRY TO FRIGHTEN US WITH YOUR SORCERER'S WAYS, LORD VADER. YOUR DEVOTION TO THAT ANCIENT RELIGION HASN'T HELPED YOU FIND THE REBELS' HIDDEN FORT-- WHHHHH!

ENOUGH OF THIS! VADER, RELEASE HIM.

AS YOU WISH!

LORD VADER WILL PROVIDE US WITH THE LOCATION OF THE REBEL FORTRESS BY THE TIME THIS STATION IS OPERATIONAL. WE WILL THEN CRUSH THE REBELLION WITH ONE SWIFT STROKE.

≥GASP≤

THE LARS HOMESTEAD...

"THESE BLAST POINTS, TOO ACCURATE FOR SAND PEOPLE. ONLY IMPERIAL STORM-TROOPERS ARE SO PRECISE."

UNCLE OWEN! AUNT BERU!

AND NOW, YOUR HIGHNESS, WE WILL DISCUSS THE LOCATION OF YOUR HIDDEN REBEL BASE.

THERE'S NOTHING YOU COULD HAVE DONE, LUKE, HAD YOU BEEN THERE.

YOU'D HAVE BEEN KILLED TOO, AND THE DROIDS WOULD NOW BE IN THE HANDS OF THE EMPIRE.

I WANT TO COME WITH YOU TO ALDERAAN. THERE'S NOTHING FOR ME HERE NOW.

I WANT TO LEARN THE WAYS OF THE FORCE. TO BECOME A JEDI LIKE MY FATHER.

SOON...

MOS EISLEY SPACEPORT. YOU WILL NEVER FIND A MORE WRETCHED HIVE OF SCUM AND VILLAINY. WE MUST BE CAUTIOUS.

I CAN'T UNDERSTAND HOW WE GOT BY THOSE TROOPS.

THE FORCE CAN HAVE A STRONG INFLUENCE ON THE WEAK-MINDED.

DO YOU REALLY THINK WE'RE GOING TO FIND A PILOT HERE THAT'LL TAKE US TO ALDERAAN?

WELL, MOST OF THE BEST FREIGHT PILOTS CAN BE FOUND HERE. ONLY WATCH YOUR STEP.

THIS PLACE CAN BE A LITTLE ROUGH.

NEGOLA DEWAGHI WOOLDUGGER?

HE DOESN'T LIKE YOU.

I'M SORRY.

I DON'T LIKE YOU EITHER.

UH!

NO BLASTERS!

AGH!

WAATT

HAN SOLO. I'M CAPTAIN OF THE MILLENNIUM FALCON. CHEWIE HERE TELLS ME YOU'RE LOOKING FOR PASSAGE TO THE ALDERAAN SYSTEM.

YES, INDEED. IF IT'S A FAST SHIP.

FAST SHIP? I'VE OUTRUN IMPERIAL STARSHIPS--THE BIG CORELLIAN SHIPS. SHE'S FAST ENOUGH FOR YOU, OLD MAN. WHAT'S THE CARGO?

ONLY PASSENGERS, MYSELF, THE BOY, TWO DROIDS. AND WE'D LIKE TO AVOID ANY IMPERIAL ENTANGLEMENTS.

WELL, THAT'S GOING TO COST YOU SOMETHING EXTRA. TEN THOUSAND, ALL IN ADVANCE.

TEN THOUSAND?! WE COULD ALMOST BUY OUR OWN SHIP FOR THAT!

BUT WHO'S GOING TO FLY IT, KID? YOU?

YOU BET I COULD! I'M NOT SUCH A BAD PILOT-- WE CAN PAY YOU TWO THOUSAND NOW, PLUS FIFTEEN WHEN WE REACH ALDERAAN.

YOU GUYS GOT YOURSELVES A SHIP.

‹GOING SOMEWHERE, SOLO?›

GREEDO! AS A MATTER OF FACT...

...I WAS JUST GOING TO SEE YOUR BOSS. TELL JABBA THAT I'VE GOT HIS MONEY.

‹IT'S TOO LATE. YOU SHOULD HAVE PAID HIM WHEN YOU HAD THE CHANCE.›

‹I'VE BEEN LOOKING FORWARD TO THIS FOR A LONG TIME...›

YES, I'LL BET YOU HAVE.

AGHHH!

SORRY ABOUT THE MESS.

‹SOLO! COME OUT OF THERE SOLO!›

RIGHT HERE, JABBA. I'VE BEEN WAITING FOR YOU.

‹HAVE YOU, NOW?›

YOU DIDN'T THINK I WAS GONNA RUN, DID YOU?

‹HAN, MY BOY, YOU DISAPPOINT ME. WHY HAVEN'T YOU PAID ME? WHY DID YOU FRY POOR GREEDO?›

LOOK, JABBA, NEXT TIME YOU WANT TO TALK TO ME, COME SEE ME YOURSELF. DON'T SEND ONE OF THESE TWERPS.

‹HAN, I CAN'T MAKE EXCEPTIONS. WHAT IF EVERYONE WHO SMUGGLED FOR ME DROPPED THEIR CARGO AT THE FIRST SIGN OF AN IMPERIAL STARSHIP? IT'S NOT GOOD FOR BUSINESS.›

LOOK, JABBA, EVEN I GET BOARDED SOMETIMES.

YOU THINK I HAD A CHOICE? I GOT A NICE EASY CHARTER NOW. PAY YOU BACK, PLUS A LITTLE EXTRA. I JUST NEED A LITTLE MORE TIME.

‹HAN, MY BOY, YOU'RE THE BEST. SO FOR AN EXTRA TWENTY PERCENT--›

FIFTEEN, JABBA. DON'T PUSH IT.

‹OKAY, FIFTEEN PERCENT. BUT IF YOU FAIL ME AGAIN, I'LL PUT A PRICE ON YOUR HEAD SO BIG YOU WON'T BE ABLE TO GO NEAR A CIVILIZED SYSTEM.›

JABBA, YOU'RE A WONDERFUL HUMAN BEING.

END OF PART ONE.

THE DEATH STAR CONTROL ROOM...

WE'VE ENTERED THE ALDERAAN SYSTEM.

GOVERNOR TARKIN. I SHOULD HAVE EXPECTED TO FIND YOU HOLDING VADER'S LEASH.

CHARMING TO THE LAST. YOU DON'T KNOW HOW HARD I FOUND IT SIGNING THE ORDER TO TERMINATE YOUR LIFE!

THE MORE YOU TIGHTEN YOUR GRIP, TARKIN, THE MORE STAR SYSTEMS WILL SLIP THROUGH YOUR FINGERS.

NOT AFTER WE DEMONSTRATE THE POWER OF THIS STATION. SINCE YOU ARE RELUCTANT TO PROVIDE US WITH THE LOCATION OF THE REBEL BASE...

...I HAVE CHOSEN TO TEST THIS STATION'S DESTRUCTIVE POWER...

...ON YOUR HOME PLANET OF ALDERAAN.

NO! ALDERAAN IS PEACEFUL! WE HAVE NO WEAPONS! YOU CAN'T POSSIBLY--

YOU WOULD PREFER ANOTHER TARGET? A MILITARY TARGET? THEN NAME THE SYSTEM! WHERE IS THE REBEL BASE?

DANTOOINE. THEY'RE ON DANTOOINE.

THERE. YOU SEE, LORD VADER, SHE CAN BE REASONABLE.

CONTINUE WITH THE OPERATION YOU MAY FIRE WHEN READY.

WHAT?

WHILE ABOARD THE MILLENNIUM FALCON...

ARE YOU ALL RIGHT? WHAT'S WRONG?

I FELT A GREAT DISTURBANCE IN THE FORCE...

...AS IF MILLIONS OF VOICES SUDDENLY CRIED OUT IN TERROR AND WERE SUDDENLY SILENCED. I FEAR SOMETHING TERRIBLE HAS HAPPENED.

WELL, YOU CAN FORGET YOUR TROUBLES WITH THOSE IMPERIAL SLUGS. I TOLD YOU I'D OUTRUN 'EM.

DON'T EVERYBODY THANK ME AT ONCE. ANYWAY, WE SHOULD BE AT ALDERAAN AT ABOUT O-TWO-HUNDRED HOURS.

REMEMBER, A JEDI CAN FEEL THE FORCE FLOWING THROUGH HIM.

YOU MEAN IT CONTROLS YOUR ACTIONS?

PARTIALLY. BUT IT ALSO OBEYS YOUR COMMANDS.

HA-HA! HOKEY RELIGIONS AND ANCIENT WEAPONS ARE NO MATCH FOR A GOOD BLASTER AT YOUR SIDE, KID.

YOU DON'T BELIEVE IN THE FORCE, DO YOU?

KID, I'VE FLOWN FROM ONE SIDE OF THIS GALAXY TO THE OTHER. I'VE SEEN A LOT OF STRANGE STUFF, BUT I'VE NEVER SEEN ANYTHING TO MAKE ME BELIEVE THERE'S ONE, ALL-POWERFUL FORCE CONTROLLING EVERYTHING.

THERE'S NO MYSTICAL ENERGY FIELD THAT CONTROLS MY DESTINY.

OUR SCOUT SHIPS HAVE REACHED DANTOOINE. THEY FOUND THE REMAINS OF A REBEL BASE, BUT THEY ESTIMATE THAT IT HAS BEEN DESERTED FOR SOME TIME. THEY ARE NOW CONDUCTING AN EXTENSIVE SEARCH OF THE SURROUNDING SYSTEMS.

SHE LIED! SHE LIED TO US!

I TOLD YOU SHE WOULD NEVER CONSCIOUSLY BETRAY THE REBELLION.

TERMINATE HER... IMMEDIATELY!

ELSEWHERE, THE MILLENNIUM FALCON EMERGES FROM HYPERSPACE...

WHAT THE...?

AW, WE'VE COME OUT OF HYPER-SPACE INTO A METEOR SHOWER. SOME KIND OF ASTEROID COLLISION. IT'S NOT ON ANY OF THE CHARTS. OUR POSITION IS CORRECT, EXCEPT... NO ALDERAAN.

WHAT DO YOU MEAN? WHERE IS IT?

THAT'S WHAT I'M TRYING TO TELL YOU, KID. IT AIN'T THERE. IT'S BEEN TOTALLY BLOWN AWAY.

DESTROYED... BY THE EMPIRE!

THERE'S ANOTHER SHIP COMING IN.

IT'S AN IMPERIAL FIGHTER.

MEEP MEEP MEEP

AND INSIDE THE MILLENNIUM FALCON...

BOY, IT'S LUCKY YOU HAD THESE COMPARTMENTS.

I USE THEM FOR SMUGGLING. THIS IS RIDICULOUS. EVEN IF I COULD TAKE OFF I'D NEVER GET PAST THE TRACTOR BEAM.

LEAVE THAT TO ME.

DAMN FOOL. I KNEW THAT YOU WERE GOING TO SAY THAT!

WHO'S THE MORE FOOLISH...THE FOOL, OR THE FOOL WHO FOLLOWS HIM?

TK-FOUR-TWO-ONE. WHY AREN'T YOU AT YOUR POST? DO YOU COPY?

TAKE OVER. WE'VE GOT A BAD TRANSMITTER. I'LL SEE WHAT I CAN DO.

ARDOOO!

ZAPT!

YOU KNOW, BETWEEN HIS HOWLING AND YOUR BLASTING EVERYTHING IN SIGHT...

...IT'S A WONDER THE WHOLE STATION DOESN'T KNOW WE'RE HERE.

SOMEBODY HAS TO SAVE OUR SKINS. INTO THE GARBAGE CHUTE, FLYBOY.

ZZZPPT

TRANG

WHAT THE HELL ARE YOU DOING?

WONDERFUL GIRL! EITHER I'M GOING TO KILL HER OR I'M BEGINNING TO LIKE HER.

I HAD EVERYTHING UNDER CONTROL UNTIL YOU LED US DOWN HERE.

YOU KNOW, IT'S NOT GOING TO TAKE THEM LONG TO FIGURE OUT WHAT HAPPENED TO US.

IT COULD BE WORSE.

IT'S WORSE.

THERE'S SOMETHING ALIVE IN HERE!

KID! LUKE! LUKE!

BLAST IT, WILL YOU? MY GUN'S JAMMED!

WHERE?

ANYWHERE! OH!

MOAN!

ZZTT

WHILE IN THE MAIN FORWARD BAY...

WHERE COULD THEY BE?

ZZZITTT

SPRANNG

I'VE BEEN WAITING FOR YOU, OBI-WAN. WE MEET AGAIN, AT LAST. THE CIRCLE IS NOW COMPLETE.

WHEN I LEFT YOU, I WAS BUT THE LEARNER; NOW I AM THE MASTER.

AROOOW

ONLY A MASTER OF EVIL, DARTH.

YOUR POWERS ARE WEAK, OLD MAN.

YOU CAN'T WIN, DARTH. IF YOU STRIKE ME DOWN, I SHALL BECOME MORE POWERFUL THAN YOU CAN POSSIBLY IMAGINE.

YOU SHOULD NOT HAVE COME BACK.

SRROWWW

BEN?

NO!

ZAROWW!

ZPPT

ZPPT

COME ON!

BLAST THE DOOR, KID!

ZPPT

RUN, LUKE, RUN!

LUKE SKYWALKER, SADDENED BY THE LOSS OF OBI-WAN KENOBI, STARES OFF INTO SPACE...

WE'RE COMING UP ON THEIR SENTRY SHIPS.

HOLD 'EM OFF! ANGLE THE DEFLECTOR SHIELDS WHILE I CHARGE UP THE MAIN GUNS!

I CAN'T BELIEVE HE'S GONE.

THERE WASN'T ANYTHING YOU COULD HAVE DONE.

COME ON, BUDD WE'RE NO OUT OF T YET!

YOU IN, KID? OKAY, STAY SHARP!

RAAAWK!

HERE THEY COME!

PEEEEU PHEUU

WHUMP

TWEET! CHIRP!

PHEWU

PHEWU

THEY'RE COMING IN TOO FAST!

WHUMP

OH!

SPROWW

DON'T WORRY, SHE'LL HOLD TOGETHER!

WE'VE LOST LATERAL CONTROLS!

YOU HEAR ME, BABY? HOLD TOGETHER!

BEEP! CHIRP!

SPRANG

SNAP

POP

PHUUUUUUU

GOT HIM! I GOT HIM!

GREAT, KID...

...DON'T GET COCKY.

THERE ARE STILL TWO MORE OF THEM OUT THERE!

SHUMM

THAT'S IT! WE DID IT!

WE DID IT!

ARE THEY AWAY?

THEY HAVE JUST MADE THE JUMP INTO HYPER-SPACE.

YOU'RE SURE THE HOMING BEACON IS SECURE ABOARD THEIR SHIP? I'M TAKING AN AWFUL RISK, VADER. THIS HAD BETTER WORK.

NOT A BAD BIT OF RESCUING, HUH? YOU KNOW, SOMETIMES I AMAZE EVEN MYSELF.

THAT DOESN'T SOUND TOO HARD. THEY LET US GO. IT'S THE ONLY EXPLANATION FOR THE EASE OF OUR ESCAPE.

EASY? YOU CALL THAT EASY?

THEY'RE TRACKING US!

NOT THIS SHIP, SISTER.

AT LEAST THE INFORMATION IN ARTOO IS STILL INTACT.

WHAT'S SO IMPORTANT? WHAT'S HE CARRYING?

THE TECHNICAL READOUTS OF THAT BATTLE-STATION. I ONLY HOPE THAT WHEN THE DATA IS ANALYZED, A WEAKNESS CAN BE FOUND. IT'S NOT OVER YET.

IT IS FOR ME, SISTER! I EXPECT TO BE WELL PAID.

I'M IN IT FOR THE MONEY.

YOU NEEDN'T WORRY ABOUT YOUR REWARD. IF MONEY IS ALL THAT YOU LOVE, THEN THAT'S WHAT YOU'LL RECEIVE.

YOUR FRIEND IS QUITE A MERCENARY. I WONDER IF HE REALLY CARES ABOUT ANYTHING...OR ANYBODY.

I CARE.

SO... WHAT DO YOU THINK OF HER, HAN?

I'M TRYING NOT TO, KID.

GOOD...

STILL, SHE'S GOT A LOT OF SPIRIT. I DON'T KNOW, WHAT DO YOU THINK?

DO YOU THINK A PRINCESS AND A GUY LIKE ME...

NO!

THE FOURTH
MOON OF
YAVIN...

THE MASSASSI
OUTPOST...

YOU'RE SAFE! WHEN
WE HEARD ABOUT
ALDERAAN, WE
FEARED THE
WORST.

WE HAVE NO TIME FOR SORROWS,
COMMANDER. YOU MUST USE
THE INFORMATION IN THIS R2-
UNIT TO HELP PLAN THE ATTACK.
IT'S OUR ONLY HOPE.

YES.

WE ARE
APPROACHING
THE PLANET YAVIN.
THE REBEL BASE
IS ON A MOON
ON THE FAR SIDE.
WE ARE PREPARING
TO ORBIT THE
PLANET.

THE BATTLE STATION IS HEAVILY SHIELDED AND CARRIES A FIREPOWER GREATER THAN HALF THE STARFLEET.

ITS DEFENSES ARE DESIGNED AROUND A DIRECT, LARGE-S ASSAULT. A SMALL, ONE-M FIGHTER SHOULD BE ABL TO PENETRATE THE OUTE DEFENSE.

PARDON ME FOR ASKING, SIR, BUT WHAT GOOD ARE SNUB-FIGHTERS GOING TO BE AGAINST THAT?

WELL, THE EMPIRE DOESN'T CONSIDER A SMALL, ONE-MAN FIGHTER TO BE ANY THREAT, OR THEY'D HAVE A TIGHTER DEFENSE.

AN ANALYSIS OF THE PLANS PROVIDED BY PRINCESS LEIA HAS DEMONSTRATED A WEAKNESS IN THE BATTLE STATION.

THE APPROACH WILL NOT BE EASY. YOU ARE REQUIRED TO MANEUVER STRAIGHT DOWN THIS TRENCH AND SKIM THE SURFACE TO THIS POINT...

...THE TARGET AREA IS ONLY TWO METERS WIDE. IT'S A SMALL, THERMAL-EXHAUST PORT, RIGHT BELOW THE MAIN PORT.

THE SHAFT LEADS DIRECTLY TO THE REACTOR SYSTEM.

A PRECISE HIT WILL START A CHAIN REACTION WHICH SHOULD DESTROY THE STATION. ONLY A PRECISE HIT WILL SET UP A CHAIN REACTION. THE SHAFT IS RAY-SHIELDED, SO YOU'LL HAVE TO USE PROTON TORPEDOES.

THAT'S IMPOSSIBLE, EVEN FOR A COMPUTER.

IT'S NOT IMPOSSIBLE.

I USED TO BULL'S-EYE WOMP RATS IN MY T-16 BACK HOME. THEY'RE NOT MUCH BIGGER THAN TWO METERS.

THEN MAN YOUR SHIPS! AND MAY THE FORCE BE WITH YOU!

THAT'S RIGHT, YEAH. I GOT SOME OLD DEBTS I GOT TO PAY OFF WITH THIS STUFF.

EVEN IF I DIDN'T, YOU DON'T THINK I'D BE FOOL ENOUGH TO STICK AROUND HERE, DO YOU?

WHY DON'T YOU COME WITH US? YOU'RE PRETTY GOOD IN A FIGHT. I COULD USE YOU.

COME ON! WHY DON'T YOU TAKE A LOOK AROUND? YOU KNOW WHAT'S ABOUT TO HAPPEN, WHAT THEY'RE UP AGAINST.

THEY COULD USE A GOOD PILOT LIKE YOU.

YOU'RE TURNING YOUR BACK ON THEM.

WHAT GOOD'S A REWARD IF YOU AIN'T AROUND TO USE IT? BESIDES, ATTACKING THE BATTLE STATION AIN'T MY IDEA OF COURAGE. IT'S MORE LIKE SUICIDE.

ALL RIGHT, WELL, TAKE CARE OF YOURSELF, HAN... I GUESS THAT'S WHAT YOU'RE BEST AT, ISN'T IT?

HEY, LUKE...

...MAY THE FORCE BE WITH YOU!

WHAT ARE YOU LOOKIN' AT? I KNOW WHAT I'M DOING.

RRMMPH!

ALL PILOTS TO YOUR STATIONS. ALL PILOTS TO YOUR STATIONS.

WHAT'S WRONG?

OH, IT'S HAN! I DON'T KNOW, I REALLY THOUGHT HE'D CHANGE HIS MIND.

HE'S GOT TO FOLLOW HIS OWN PATH. NO ONE CAN CHOOSE IT FOR HIM.

I ONLY WISH BEN WERE HERE.

HEY, THIS R2 UNIT OF YOURS SEEMS A BIT BEAT-UP. DO YOU WANT A NEW ONE?

NOT ON YOUR LIFE! THAT LITTLE DROID AND I HAVE BEEN THROUGH A LOT TOGETHER.

YOU OKAY, ARTOO?

BEEP! TWWP!

GOOD.

LUKE,
THE FORCE
WILL BE
WITH YOU.

VAH-ROOOOMM

STANDBY ALERT. DEATH STAR APPROACHING. ESTIMATED TIME TO FIRING RANGE-- FIFTEEN MINUTES.

THE DEATH STAR MOVES SLOWLY INTO POSITION BEHIND THE MASSIVE, YELLOW SURFACE OF YAVIN...

SHEWW

LUKE ADJUSTS HIS CONTROLS AS THE SHIPS BEGIN TO BE BUFFETED SLIGHTLY.

SWITCH YOUR DEFLECTORS ON.

DOUBLE FRONT!

AS THE REBEL FIGHTERS APPROACH, COMPLEX PATTERNS ON THE DEATH STAR'S METALLIC SURFACE BEGIN TO BECOME VISIBLE...

LOOK AT THE SIZE OF THAT THING!

CUT THE CHATTER, RED TWO!

ACCELERATE TO ATTACK SPEED.

AS THE FIGHTERS MOVE CLOSER TO THE DEATH STAR, THE AWESOME SIZE OF THE GARGANTUAN IMPERIAL FORTRESS IS REVEALED...

APPROACHING THE DEATH STAR...

THIS IS IT, BOYS!

RED LEADER, THIS IS GOLD LEADER.

I COPY, GOLD LEADER.

WE'RE STARTING FOR THE TARGET SHAFT NOW.

WE'RE IN POSITION. I'M GOING TO CUT ACROSS THE AXIS AND TRY AND DRAW THEIR FIRE.

TWO SQUADS OF REBEL
FIGHTERS PEEL OFF. THE
X-WINGS DIVE TOWARD THE
DEATH STAR SURFACE...

SHROOOM

ARE YOU ALL RIGHT?

I GOT A LITTLE COOKED, BUT I'M OKAY.

WE COUNT THIRTY REBEL SHIPS, LORD VADER, BUT THEY'RE SO SMALL THEY'RE EVADING OUR TURBOLASERS!

WE'LL HAVE TO DESTROY THEM SHIP TO SHIP. GET THE CREWS TO THEIR FIGHTERS.

WATCH YOURSELF! THERE'S A LOT OF FIRE COMING FROM THE RIGHT SIDE OF THAT DEFLECTION TOWER.

I'M ON IT.

I'M GOING IN. COVER ME, PORKINS!

I'M RIGHT WITH YOU, RED THREE.

HERE THEY COME.

WATCH IT! YOU'VE GOT ONE ON YOUR TAIL.

SPAROW

SPAROW

KAWHOM

BIGGS! YOU'VE PICKED ONE UP... WATCH IT!

I CAN'T SEE IT!

THEY'RE ON ME TIGHT, I CAN'T SHAKE HIM...

I'LL BE RIGHT THERE.

WHOM

THIS IS GOLD LEADER. WE'RE STARTING OUR ATTACK RUN.

I COPY GOLD LEADER. MOVE INTO POSITION.

STAY IN ATTACK FORMATION!

THE EXHAUST PORT IS MARKED AND LOCKED IN.

WHUP

SWITCH ALL POWER TO FRONT DEFLECTOR SCREENS.

DEATH STAR WILL BE IN RANGE IN FIVE MINUTES.

GOLD FIVE TO RED LEADER...LOST TIREE, LOST HUTCH.

I COPY, GOLD LEADER.

THEY CAME FROM BEHIND...

WHAM

SKEEE

WE'VE ANALYZED THEIR ATTACK, SIR, AND THERE IS A DANGER. SHOULD I HAVE YOUR SHIP STANDING BY?

EVACUATE? IN OUR MOMENT OF TRIUMPH? I THINK YOU OVERESTIMATE THEIR CHANCES!

RED BOYS, THIS IS RED LEADER. RENDEZVOUS AT MARK SIX POINT ONE.

THIS IS RED TWO. FLYING TOWARDS YOU.

RED THREE STANDING BY.

RED LEADER, THIS IS BASE ONE. KEEP HALF YOUR GROUP OUT OF RANGE FOR THE NEXT RUN.

COPY, BASE ONE. LUKE, TAKE RED TWO AND THREE. HOLD UP HERE AND WAIT FOR MY SIGNAL TO START YOUR RUN.

THIS IS IT!

WHUP

WHUP

WE SHOULD BE ABLE TO SEE IT BY NOW.

KEEP YOUR EYES OPEN FOR THOSE FIGHTERS!

THERE'S TOO MUCH INTERFERENCE! RED FIVE, CAN YOU SEE THEM FROM WHERE YOU ARE?

NO SIGN OF ANY... WAIT! COMING IN POINT THREE FIVE.

I SEE THEM.

TARGET'S COMING UP! JUST HOLD THEM OFF FOR A FEW SECONDS.

CLOSE UP FORMATION.

NEGATIVE. IT DIDN'T GO IN, JUST IMPACTED ON THE SURFACE.

I JUST LOST MY STARBOARD ENGINE. GET SET UP FOR YOUR ATTACK RUN.

VIP

VIP

WHOOM

REBEL BASE, ONE MINUTE AND CLOSING.

BIGGS, WEDGE, LET'S CLOSE IT UP. WE'RE GOING IN FULL THROTTLE. THAT OUGHT TO KEEP THOSE FIGHTERS OFF OUR BACKS.

RIGHT WITH YOU, BOSS.

LUKE, AT THAT SPEED WILL YOU BE ABLE TO PULL OUT IN TIME?

IT'LL BE JUST LIKE BEGGAR'S CANYON BACK HOME.

WATCH YOURSELF! INCREASE SPEED FULL THROTTLE!

WHAT ABOUT THAT TOWER?

YOU WORRY ABOUT THOSE FIGHTERS! I'LL WORRY ABOUT THE TOWER!

ARTOO... THAT STABILIZER'S BROKEN LOOSE AGAIN. SEE IF YOU CAN'T LOCK IT DOWN!

FIGHTERS. COMING IN, POINT THREE.

WREEEEE

I'M HIT! I CAN'T STAY WITH YOU.

GET CLEAR, WEDGE! YOU CAN'T DO ANY MORE GOOD BACK THERE!

SORRY!

LET HIM GO! STAY ON THE LEADER.

HURRY, LUKE, THEY'RE COMING IN MUCH FASTER THIS TIME. WE CAN'T HOLD THEM!

ARTOO, TRY AND INCREASE THE POWER!

SQUEEE!

I'VE LOST ARTOO!

THE DEATH STAR HAS CLEARED THE PLANET. THE DEATH STAR HAS CLEARED THE PLANET.

REBEL BASE, IN RANGE.

YOU MAY FIRE WHEN READY.

I HAVE YOU NOW.

WHAT?

YAHOO!

KHARANG!

WHOOM

YOU'RE ALL CLEAR, KID! NOW LET'S BLOW THIS THING AND GO HOME!

The creative team behind *A New Hope* The Special Edition

Bruce Jones was born behind a four-color press in Hackensack, New Jersey. Kidnapped at birth and raised by gypsies, the exact date of his birth is unknown, though dental records suggest it was sometime before the discovery of fluoride. His early career included a stint as a male nurse at a hospital for recovering alcoholics and brain-surgery patients, during which he coined the now oft-quoted phrase: "All things considered, I'd rather have a bottle in front of me, than a frontal lobotomy." Somehow, during his busy schedule of emptying drool cups, he found time to work on projects like *Amazing Stories*, *Creepy*, *Eerie*, *Vampirella*, and *Twisted Tales* to name a few. In recent months, Mr. Jones made headlines when witnesses reported him wrestled, by police, to the floor of the New York Stock Exchange, cursing vehemently and waving a pair of old sweat socks in the air. "I only wanted to exchange them for some argyles!" he was reported as screaming.

Although **Eduardo Barreto**'s work is new to the realm of *Star Wars*, he considers himself an "old workhorse" since he began his comics-publishing career 26 years ago at the age of 16. Barreto has worked for Marvel Comics, DC Comics, Archie Comics, Western Publishing, Tekno•Comix, and a host of European and South American companies and has illustrated a long list of characters including Superman, Batman, Indiana Jones, Aliens, Predator, and Mickey Spillane's Mike Danger. "I enjoy working in comics," says Barreto, "because there is a lot more creative freedom than there is in advertising or animation." He is thrilled to be working on *Star Wars* and is especially thrilled to be working with Al Williamson. Barreto lives in Montevideo, Uruguay with his wife and three children.

Al Williamson has been drawing comics for "110 years," and, he says, "if they want me to quit, they'll have to shoot me." Williamson's love for drawing comics is evidenced in his illustrations of some of comics' most famous characters. He assisted Burne Hogarth on the "Tarzan" strips, drew *Flash Gordon* for King Features and recently for Marvel Comics, contributed to the *Superman* mythos for DC Comics, and illustrated *Science Fiction* comics for EC. It was Williamson's depiction of Flash that caught the fancy of George Lucas who commissioned Al to do the (now) classic-strip adaptations of *Star Wars*. Williamson worked with writer Archie Goodwin and sometimes used his own son and daughter — Victor and Valerie — as models. Williamson and his lovely wife Corina make their home in Pennsylvania.

Best known for their collective work on the original movie poster for *Star Wars*, **Tim** and **Greg Hildebrandt** have enjoyed careers together (as the Brothers Hildebrandt) and separately. They won the Golden Eagle Award for their film *Project Hope* and are the award-winning illustrators of such well-known properties as *Star Wars*, *The Lord of the Rings*, *The Sword of Shanarra*, *Barbarella*, *The Clash of the Titans*, and *The Secret of N.I.M.H.* Individually, Greg's illustrations have graced magazines *Omni* and *Heavy Metal* and over a dozen children's fairy-tale classics. His cover for a *Spectre* comic won DC's Cover of the Month Award. Tim has painted art calendars for *Dungeons and Dragons*, *Realms of Wonder*, and *The Dragonriders of Pern*. He's also painted covers for numerous science-fiction and fantasy magazines and books.

Dave Dorman is an Eisner award-winning illustrator best known for his photo-realistic renderings of action and fantasy subjects on such titles as *Batman* for DC Comics; the *Indiana Jones* and *Star Wars* series for Dark Horse; and *Aliens: Tribes*, an illustrated novel also for Dark Horse. His mass-market book covers include the best-selling series *Young Jedi Knights*, *Aliens*, *Lone Wolf*, *Surfing Samurai Robots*, and many others. Dorman has also done trading cards for Skybox, Topps, and Fleer; toy design for Hasbro Toys; motion-picture pre-production art; and motion-based ride conceptual art. Dorman's captivating cover art from the *A New Hope* comic-book series is featured on the following pages. If you look closely, you will see that the covers are actually four separate quadrants of a single painting